WHO'S AFRAID OF THE
MULTIVERSE?

Jeffrey A. Zweerink, Ph.D.

CONTENTS

AUTHOR'S NOTE

"Isn't the multiverse a threat to the Christian faith—or at least to our apologetic efforts?" Whether explicitly asked, defensively rebutted, or quietly suppressed for fear it might be true, this question often arises when Christians discuss the multiverse. I know it was my concern when, nearly a decade ago, I first began to encounter multiverse ideas.

Since that time, I have sought to understand why scientists (and non-scientists) find multiverse models appealing. A wise pastor once encouraged me never to argue *against* a viewpoint until I understood it well enough to argue *for* it. Consequently, I tried to put myself in the proverbial shoes of a multiverse advocate during my studies. Since this booklet flows from those studies, I write from the standpoint of one who believes a multiverse exists.

In the first half of the booklet, I explain what the term "multiverse" means and how the multiverse theory impacts Christian scientific apologetics—namely the cosmological and teleological arguments. Because I write in a way that seems to argue for the multiverse, the first half of this booklet may cause considerable tension. However, I encourage you to keep reading until the end. You will find, as I did, that the scientific research into multiverse models ultimately strengthens apologetics arguments for the Christian faith. Admittedly, the arguments become more subtle and sophisticated, but multiverse research also makes those arguments more robust and versatile.

Another reason I write as if the multiverse might exist is that we still have much to learn in cosmology. One hundred years ago, few thought that other planets beyond the solar system or galaxies beyond the Milky Way actually existed. After all, no mention of such objects occurs in the Bible. In fact, the discovery of these objects impacted significant apologetics arguments—primarily the teleological argument (the argument from design). However, no right-thinking Christian today need be troubled by discoveries of new planets and galaxies.

Similarly, as I look through Scripture, I find nothing that rules out the existence of a multiverse. What I do find is that no matter how large this creation proves to be, it owes its existence, in every respect, to the creative acts of God. From an apologetics perspective, the key question is not "Does the multiverse exist?" but "Would the existence of the multiverse diminish the case for the truth of Christianity?"

Without giving away the details, the material in this booklet argues that, whether or not the multiverse exists, the case for the Christian faith grows stronger with each new cosmological discovery.

As with most scientific challenges raised in the last hundred years, what initially seemed a threat to Christianity ultimately stands in strong support. This booklet seeks to demonstrate how the multiverse question fits this pattern so that you can address skeptics' concerns with gentleness and respect—and without fear.

A Long Time Ago, In A Galaxy Far, Far Away...

Most people probably remember the first time they saw *Star Wars*. I know I do. Who can forget an epic battle between good and evil involving numerous civilizations populating a distant galaxy—all portrayed with unprecedented special effects? The dedication and diversity of the film's fans testify to *Star Wars'* broad appeal. Part of this allure flows from our innate curiosity about possible other worlds.

In the *Star Wars* galaxy, human beings reside on different planets and moons, alongside a diverse array of intelligent nonhuman life-forms. Han Solo, the rogue spice smuggler who transports protagonist Luke Skywalker and his companions, pilots his ship with the help of a physically powerful, ape-like Wookiee named Chewbacca. An obese slug-like Hutt named Jabba has placed a bounty on Han's head. The band playing at the space-port where Luke and Han first meet features the musically gifted Bith with a stereotypical Martian appearance. Numerous sentient and intellectually talented androids aid the good guys in their quest to defeat the evil Galactic Empire. And, the list goes on. Life abounds in this far-away galaxy!

During the thirty-plus years since *Star Wars* debuted on the big screen, another idea, even more radical than the science fiction world of the film, has attracted the attention and support of many naturalists. Some argue that current cosmological observations and theories directly imply that the universe we occupy is one of a vast multitude that lies beyond detection. The implications of such a "multiverse" impact several arguments used in support of a supernatural Creator. If the multiverse exists, it may explain the apparent fine-tuning of this universe in purely naturalistic terms, making the idea of a Designer obsolete. Could this multiverse have existed forever, removing the need for a beginning—and a Beginner?

The following discussion will, quite literally, greatly expand your universe. New ideas and terminology are required. Challenging concepts may prompt you to reevaluate and refine some of your favorite apologetics arguments. However, rewards await those who wade through the details and face the challenges. The resultant understanding will ultimately strengthen your faith as well as equip you to engage others on this topic. So let's buckle up to begin our journey through the multiverse and see if we can't sort out the fact from the science fiction.

PREPARING FOR LIFTOFF

B efore embarking on our journey, two questions must be answered: What is the universe, and what does complex life require?

WHAT IS THE UNIVERSE?

According to Carl Sagan, a devout naturalist, "the Cosmos is all that is or ever was or ever will be."[1] However, an adequate multiverse discussion requires more precise terms. Presumably, the fictitious galaxy of *Star Wars* resides in our universe, and only technological barriers prevent astronomers from observing it. In reality, however, the laws of physics place a fundamental limit on the extent of the universe that Earth-bound astronomers can see.

Light travels through space at a specific speed. Because the universe is only fourteen billion years old, only light emitted from objects within some maximum distance can reach Earth. Thus, astronomers define a region called the "observable universe" that includes all locations within this maximum distance.

Although the universe has continually expanded since moments after the big bang, the expansion rate has been slower than the speed of light. Therefore, the amount of observable matter and energy within the observable universe has grown with time. However, astronomers now know the expansion of the universe has been accelerating for the last five billion years. The expansion rate at the farthest reaches that astronomers can observe already approaches the speed of light and will eventually exceed it. Consequently, the amount of matter and energy within the observable universe will decrease in the future.

Three points about the observable universe merit mention. First, the size of the observable universe grows over time because light travels farther as the universe ages. Second, the amount of matter and energy in the observable universe shrinks with time once the expansion rate exceeds the speed of light.

Third, space does not end at the edge of the observable universe, but astronomers on Earth can never directly detect anything beyond the edge. Without evidence to indicate otherwise, the same laws of physics operating within the observable universe govern regions existing beyond the observable universe. The term "universe" refers to all regions governed by these laws.

WHAT DOES COMPLEX LIFE REQUIRE?

The extent to which this universe appears designed to support complex life explains why some scientists embrace the multiverse theory. Over the centuries, many people have argued that the universe seems designed specifically as a habitat for humans. Scientists know this idea as the anthropic principle and generally acknowledge the remarkable way this universe supports life. In the last one hundred years or so, significant scientific discoveries have increasingly revealed numerous fine-tuned details that affirm the biblical description of the cosmos. Some examples of the conclusions drawn by various secular scientists follow.

In *Just Six Numbers*, Sir Martin Rees, an international leader in cosmology at Trinity College at the University of Cambridge, points out six numbers, set in the earliest moments of creation, that take on values essential to life.[2] For example, even small changes in the number of large spatial dimensions or in the strength of the gravitational force compared to the electromagnetic force lead to an uninhabitable universe.

Michael Denton, former senior research fellow in human molecular genetics at New Zealand's University of Otago, discusses in his book *Nature's Destiny* the many aspects of this universe upon which life depends.[3] In particular, Denton fleshes out life's dependency on the critical building blocks this universe provides—carbon, oxygen, planets, and so forth.

Even starting with a universe governed by laws that permit life does not demand that life—especially complex life like human beings—would come to exist. Peter Ward and Donald Brownlee explore this idea further in their book *Rare Earth*.[4] One theme they develop pertains to habitable zones. The requirements of complex life place a number of constraints on the possible sites where life could exist.

For example, the liquid water required for life's biochemical reactions restricts life to locations with an adequate heat supply that can melt a substantial amount of ice into water without completely vaporizing it. This requirement rules out the surfaces of stars and the bulk of interstellar space and interstellar bodies as possible life sites. It also places significant limitations on the heavy element composition of any planet where complex life might live.

Additionally, regions of high cosmic radiation, such as in the inner parts of galaxies and regions where star formation ceased long ago, as in globular clusters, are also excluded as habitable zones. Finding a planet inside all the required habitable zones simultaneously puts tight constraints on the likelihood of life's arising in this universe strictly by natural processes.

In *What if the Moon Didn't Exist?* Neil Comins, physics professor at the University of Maine, explores bodies much closer to home.[5] This book outlines the adverse effects of changing the size of various bodies in the solar system such as the Moon, Sun, Earth, or Jupiter. In each case, any significant change in the solar system configuration would result in a dramatic reduction of Earth's capacity to support complex life.

The Anthropic Cosmological Principle by John Barrow, professor of mathematical sciences at the University of Cambridge, and Frank Tipler, professor of mathematical physics at Tulane University, provides the most comprehensive treatment available through the mid 1980s of the universe's habitability.[6] Barrow's more recent book, *The Constants of Nature*, updates many of the fine-tuning arguments with scientific advances in the intervening twenty years.[7] For further study of these fine-tuned details, see also *The Creator and the Cosmos* and *Why the Universe Is the Way It Is*, by Hugh Ross.[8] A lengthy catalog of finely tuned aspects of our universe and how they support complex life can be found at www.designevidences.org.

These resources highlight the noncontroversial nature of the idea that the universe *appears* finely tuned to support complex life, such as humans. The long-standing debate between creationism and naturalism centers on whether the universe exhibits design or merely the appearance of design.

THE MULTIVERSE LANDSCAPE

NECESSARY EQUIPMENT FOR THE VOYAGE

To be successful, this journey through the multiverse requires the proper equipment. Two important scientific concepts figure prominently in building most multiverse models. First, scientists have an abundance of evidence that indicates the universe experienced inflation—a brief period of hyperfast expansion early in the universe's history. Second, ongoing research indicates that the four fundamental forces—gravitational, electromagnetic, and the strong and weak nuclear forces—can be unified within a single theoretical framework. String theory currently represents the most popular of the many models attempting to unify all the fundamental forces.

Inflation

Before the addition of inflation to big bang cosmology, three major observational problems plagued the theory. First, the discovery of the cosmic microwave background (CMB) radiation and its subsequent characterization demonstrated a remarkable degree of uniformity in the observable universe. No matter which direction astronomers looked, they measured the same temperature. However, with an expansion rate slower than the speed of light and a 14-billion-year-old universe, the distance between regions in opposite directions meant that light could not travel between the regions in order to establish a common temperature. Scientists term this the "horizon problem."

Second, even without understanding all the types of matter and energy in the universe, astronomers realized the geometry of the observable universe was extremely close to flat (see "What is Flat?" sidebar). The discovery of ripples in the CMB (see figure 1, page 10) confirmed an essentially flat geometry, while the discovery of dark matter and dark energy (or space-energy density) determined all the constituents of the universe.[9] However, an almost flat geometry is unstable over time in the same way a rod balanced on end is unstable. Just as slight deviation from vertical sends the rod rapidly crashing to the ground, so any slight deviation from "flat" during its early moments drives the observable universe quickly toward either zero density or infinite density. Scientists term this the "flatness problem."

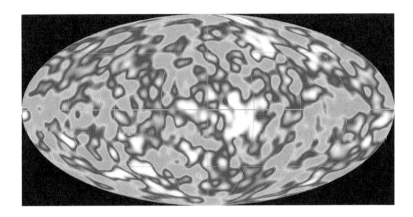

Figure 1. The ripples in the CMB first detected by the COBE satellite reflect small temperature variations present in the early universe. Courtesy of NASA

As physicists worked on a theory that unified (see the next section) the strong nuclear interaction with the electromagnetic and weak nuclear forces under a common framework, a number of unwieldy details emerged. Most notably, the theory predicted the formation of a multitude of cosmic defects when the two forces separated as the universe cooled. Scientists refer to the most prevalent defects as magnetic monopoles. Monopoles are magnets with only one polarity instead of both north and south polarity like normal magnets. Astronomers have searched for monopoles but found none. The lack of detectable magnetic monopoles placed strong limits on the actual number of monopoles in the observable universe, far below the amount predicted by the unified theories. Scientists term this the "monopole problem."

Inflation solves all three problems. The hyperfast expansion at the start of the universe takes small regions with the same temperature and expands them to a size compatible with the observable universe. Inflation also drives the geometry of the universe exquisitely close to flat. Since inflation occurs around the same time as the separation of the strong and electroweak forces, it also dilutes the magnetic monopole concentration to a level below astronomers' measured limits.

Unification and String Theory

In *The Bourne Identity* Jason Bourne is a man without an identity. He finds himself on a fishing boat recovering from gunshot wounds and a case of severe amnesia. He soon realizes he has access to a safety deposit box with enormous financial reserves and numerous passports. He also possesses extraordinary physical skills

WHAT IS FLAT?

A cosmologist uses "flat," as opposed to "closed" or "open," to describe the geometry of the spatial dimensions of the universe. By analogy, a piece of paper is flat whereas a ball (closed geometry) and a saddle (open geometry) are both curved. Since astronomers cannot view the universe from the outside, a more observationally useful definition involves how two parallel laser beams travel through space. The distance between the beams as they travel falls into one of three categories: (1) in a closed geometry the beams move closer together; (2) in an open geometry they move farther apart; (3) in a geometrically flat universe, two parallel beams remain separated by the same distance, never intersecting regardless of how far they travel. ©Mark Garlick/Photo Researchers, Inc. and Aaron Garcia

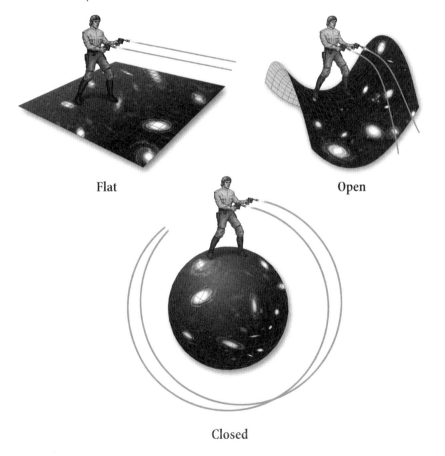

Flat

Open

Closed

and an intuition for escaping the most difficult circumstances. Most puzzling to Jason are his fleeting memories of an otherwise elusive past and the assassins chasing him. Throughout the film Jason seeks to develop an explanation that properly integrates all these disparate remnants of his life.

Likewise, scientists often work to explain seemingly unconnected ideas under a common theoretical framework. This process, known as unification, has played a major role in driving scientific advancement. Isaac Newton first unified the forces that governed objects on Earth with those in the heavens. James Clerk Maxwell continued the process by showing that electricity and magnetism are different manifestations of a common electromagnetic force. Albert Einstein explicitly integrated into his theory of special relativity the concept that the laws governing motion don't depend on an observer's location or motion. This work by Einstein led scientists to realize that matter can transform to energy and vice-versa, as embodied in his well-known formula, $E=mc^2$.

Theorists in the 1970s unified the electromagnetic and weak nuclear forces under a common theoretical umbrella, the electroweak force. A number of grand unified theories (GUTs) seek to expand the umbrella to include the strong nuclear force. A vigorous experimental program exists to determine which—if any—of the dozen or more GUTs best represent reality. However, the most difficult unification arises when scientists try to integrate gravity with the other forces.

Some background will help elucidate the heart of the problem. In the early 1900s scientists were just discovering experimental results unexplainable within the classical picture of nature. In this familiar picture, no limits existed to how finely various quantities, such as the energy or momentum of a particle, could be divided. In other words, the classical picture viewed these quantities as continuous. However, the emerging quantum mechanical revolution described a universe where these quantities came in discrete bundles. Stated another way, classical physics pictured the world as a smooth, continuous slide, but quantum mechanics depicted matter and energy as a staircase with discrete incremental steps. The theories describing the electromagnetic and nuclear interactions are all quantum mechanical in nature. Yet while the quantum world viewed matter and energy as discrete, space and time were still considered continuous.

Before Einstein developed the theory of general relativity to describe the gravitational force, scientists viewed space and time as absolute. Matter moved through space but did not affect it in any way. And time moved inexorably forward regardless of any physical processes at work. Not only does the theory of general relativity treat space and time on common ground, it radically changes scientists' picture of them. As matter and energy move, they affect the space-time in which they travel. According to general relativity, physical processes stretch, bend, and warp space-time. However, in its current formulation, general relativity requires a continuous space-time.

As bizarre as the quantum mechanical and relativistic pictures of the universe seem, scientists have confirmed these theories' validity to extraordinary precision in every technically feasible way.[10] Testing continues vigorously even today. Still, a problem arises when scientists try to determine how the earliest moments of the universe unfold.

The strong gravitational fields arising from the immense density during this fleeting period mandate that scientists account for relativistic processes. The small size of the observable universe mandates that quantum mechanical effects be included also. Yet the continuous nature of general relativity and the discrete nature of quantum mechanics are mutually incompatible. Thus, scientists need a more complete theory—one that unites quantum mechanics with general relativity—to adequately understand the very early universe. Einstein's theory of general relativity expanded upon the usefulness of Newton's work in understanding gravity. In a similar fashion, scientists expect the theory that unifies general relativity and quantum mechanics to build upon the successes of both.

String theory stands as the most popular, though certainly not the only, theory to attempt this unification. Instead of viewing fundamental particles (such as electrons, quarks, or neutrinos) as "point" particles, string theory posits that these particles are actually loops of "string" with some minimum size. This minimum size imposes a fundamental length scale above which all physical processes operate. When scientists calculate where any discreteness in space-time would occur, they get sizes smaller than this fundamental length scale. Consequently, conditions never arise where general relativity and quantum mechanics cannot both operate properly—even in the conditions of the early universe.[11]

This unification does require the existence of additional space dimensions. Given that this observable universe exhibits three spatial and one time dimension, string theory seems unrealistic. Fortunately for string theorists, a mechanism exists within the theory for limiting the size of these extra dimensions. So, string theory posits that we live in nine or ten space dimensions, three of which are expanding as the rest remain small enough that they have not yet affected observations of our universe.

Now that we're equipped with such concepts as inflation and the unification of the four fundamental forces of the universe, we're ready to embark on our journey through the multiverse.

MAPPING THE MULTIVERSE

The word "multiverse" means several things, but they all share a common thread. Each definition requires the existence of other regions beyond the observable universe. Some multiverse theories propose regions with different laws of physics while others propose that the physical laws match our own. Max Tegmark, an MIT physicist, has categorized multiverse models into four levels—each with an increasing degree of speculation.[12] Our journey begins with the least speculative.

Level I—A Ginormous Universe

Consider again the far, far away galaxy of *Star Wars*. Scientists can define an observable universe for Luke Skywalker's home planet just as they do for Earth.[13] These two observable universes might overlap and also contain regions unique to each. If Luke's planet resided at the edge of our observable universe, one could envision another galaxy on the far side of Luke's observable universe. As figure 2 shows, our observable universe is completely separate from an observable universe centered on Galaxy X.

Such a scenario describes the Level I multiverse.

The only real controversial aspect of Level I is its spatial extent, or size. In this model, the size of the universe determines how many distinct observable universes exist. Based on measurable characteristics of the observable universe (such as its physical dimensions and the maximum allowed curvature), the region beyond the observation horizon is at least one thousand times larger than the observable universe.[14] Thus, at least one thousand regions the size of our observable universe exist within the total universe!

Measurements indicate a minimum limit of one thousand times the size of the observable universe but no upper limit exists. Many scientists argue for a spatially infinite—one that goes on forever in all directions—total universe with a finite age.

Generally, scientists expect all regions of the Level I multiverse to exhibit the same physical laws with the same constants. That convention will be upheld here unless specifically noted. In fact, the Level I multiverse and the universe are synonymous.

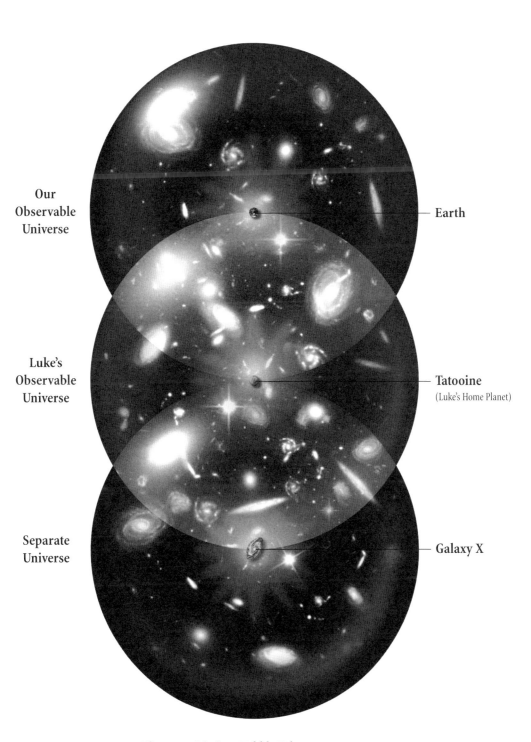

Our
Observable
Universe

Earth

Luke's
Observable
Universe

Tatooine
(Luke's Home Planet)

Separate
Universe

Galaxy X

Figure 2. Distinct Hubble Volumes ©Aaron Garcia

Calling the Level I a "multiverse" is somewhat of a misnomer because all observable volumes are really part of the same large universe. Consequently, many scientists prefer to reserve the term "multiverse" for far more speculative scenarios that posit the existence of other completely separate universes.

Evidence Supporting Level I

While the multitude of unobservable regions in the Level I multiverse may sound bizarre or contrived, in 1965 scientists began discovering evidence supporting it. Arno Penzias and Robert Wilson detected an unexpected and unexplained background signal using a microwave receiver. Failing to find the source of this background signal after an exhaustive study, they eventually concluded that the microwave emission originated in space. Soon, they realized this microwave background radiation represented the glowing embers of the universe's big bang creation event. The magnitude of this discovery garnered a Nobel Prize for Penzias and Wilson in 1978.

More detailed studies of CMB radiation revealed an astonishing uniformity. The CMB radiation looked identical in every direction. Recall the horizon problem discussed earlier. Distant points in the observable universe had not had enough time to communicate in order to have the same temperature.

Consider what happens after lighting the fireplace in a living room. A large temperature difference exists when comparing the fireplace with the corner on the other side of the room. However, after enough time elapses the heat penetrates the whole room creating nearly uniform temperatures everywhere.

The room exhibits uniform temperatures because enough time passes for the various parts of the room to "communicate" and equalize the heat. As with the heat in the living room, the uniformity of the CMB radiation (which corresponds to a temperature) requires enough time for the various regions of the observable universe to communicate with one another.

The distance between the farthest observable points in two opposite directions exceeds the distance light can travel in the time since the big bang. But the farthest points in two opposite directions measure the same temperature even though light cannot travel between them. Scientists say these two points are not in causal contact because of the impossibility of any communication between them. In fact, one can easily show that any two points not in causal contact now were never in causal contact—assuming the universe always expanded at a rate slower than the speed of light.[15]

Fast forward to April 1992. NASA had just released the astonishing results from the first year of data collected by the Cosmic Background Explorer (COBE). The announcement provided dramatic confirmation of many big bang cosmology predictions. Most significantly, COBE detected ripples in the remarkably uniform CMB (see figure 1, page 10). Big bang cosmology required these ripples (caused by temperature fluctuations in the early universe) in order to explain the development of galaxies and clusters of galaxies astronomers observe today. Additionally, the characteristic size of the ripples permitted the COBE team to determine the geometry of space. The geometry matched scientists' expectations of a flat universe. Like Penzias and Wilson, the leaders of the COBE team, John Mather and George Smoot, received a Nobel Prize in 2006 for the discovery of the CMB ripples.

The level of CMB uniformity and the characteristics of its ripples validated cosmologists' idea that the universe underwent a period of hyperfast expansion (inflation) very early in its history.[16] Not only does this evidence validate big bang cosmology, but it also implies the existence of the Level I multiverse.

During inflation the universe grew by an enormous factor (more than 10^{26} times) in the minutest fraction of a second. This faster-than-light expansion took regions of space that were once in causal contact and separated them by distances so large that light would never be able to traverse them during the history of the universe.[17] In other words, regions within the observable universe *before* inflation were carried beyond our observable universe *during* inflation. Thus, space does not end at the farthest distances astronomers can see. The regions beyond astronomers' observational reach constitute the Level I multiverse.

Level II—A Portal to Other Worlds

The movie *The Chronicles of Narnia: The Lion, the Witch and the Wardrobe* opens with four siblings running for shelter from a blitzkrieg over WWII London. Soon after, the children are sent to live in a country mansion, far from danger. While hiding from the housekeeper in a large wardrobe, Peter, Susan, Edmund, and Lucy open the door into a strange land called Narnia where winter never ceases and animals can talk with humans.

A powerful witch rules the land and subjects its inhabitants to her cruel whims and desires. With Aslan the Lion's help, the children battle to free the citizens (and the land) from the oppressive regime of the White Witch. After their victory, the brothers and sisters reign as the kings and queens of Narnia for many years before eventually returning through the wardrobe to the country mansion. To their great surprise, no time has passed in England despite their long stay in Narnia.

Because some laws of physics operate differently there, Narnia represents a different universe. When the children stepped in and out of the wardrobe, they entered completely different space-time realms. Figure 3 illustrates this imagery of the Level II multiverse, which is what most scientists envision when using the term "multiverse."

The limits of observation in a *single* universe define the Level I multiverse. In the Level II multiverse, *multiple* universes, presumably with different laws of physics, exist.

Figure 3. Level II Multiverse ©Aaron Garcia

Evidence Supporting Level II

When scientists first proposed a period of inflation, the picture of the early universe differed from that of today. In the traditional picture, some sort of physical process drove the universe through an incredibly brief period of hyperfast expansion immediately after the big bang creation event. This inflation ensured that astronomers would see the flat, uniform universe they observe.

Although scientists knew of mechanisms capable of driving inflation, they lacked a theory describing the precise details of how these mechanisms worked. Not until the mid-1990s did a viable theory arise that began to fill in those details. That theory proposed a dramatic reordering of early universe events.

While scientists knew how to start inflation, getting inflation to end in a way that produced the observed universe proved more difficult. Any mechanism to drive inflation once the total universe started would inevitably terminate at different times in different locations. Consequently, these differences would generate a universe far clumpier than we observe. It is analogous to a pot of boiling water. The water does not boil by forming a single (uniform) bubble. Instead bunches of bubbles form, making the water appear irregular and "clumpy." Furthermore, without extreme fine-tuning of the inflation-ending processes, this unevenness would produce uninhabitable universes filled with massive black holes and regions completely devoid of matter.[18]

However, all the fine-tuning disappears in a different scenario. Imagine the mechanism driving inflation operating in some über-space before the creation of our total universe (see figure 4, page 20). This über-space expands very rapidly, but in some locations the mechanism driving inflation stops. These regions where inflation has stopped would grow over time. Scientists can calculate how this scenario looked from within one of the "bubbles" where inflation ceased. Doing the proper calculations, they get a picture that reproduces all the observations astronomers make of our own universe.

The region inside a single bubble exhibits the uniformity seen in this universe, even though the inside of the other bubbles would appear different from ours. Although the vast majority of these bubbles would differ radically from our universe, most multiverse advocates expect any possible manifestation of the physical laws to appear in at least one bubble. This scenario for inflation dramatically changes scientists' concept of the universe.[19]

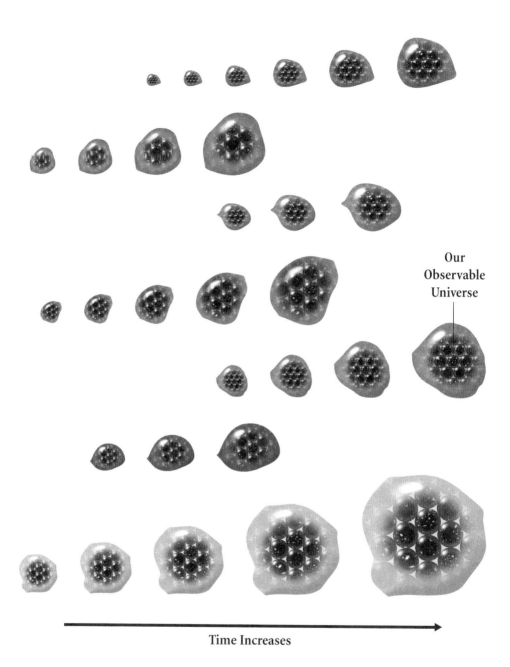

Figure 4. Inflation forming bubble universes ©Aaron Garcia

First, if this scenario proves true, then inflation predates the existence of our universe instead of occurring within our universe. Second, the boundary of our own bubble represents the big bang. Third, if inflation ends in more than one place, then other "bubble universes" with potentially different laws of physics and fundamental constants exist. This collection of "bubble universes" represents the Level II multiverse.

Levels I and II are not mutually exclusive. In fact, any bubble universe in the Level II picture that undergoes inflationary expansion would exhibit a Level I multiverse as well. However, the evidential basis for Level II pales compared to that for Level I. Considerable evidence points to an inflationary epoch in the known universe and that evidence is sufficient to establish the existence of a Level I multiverse. By contrast, the Level II multiverse relies on a particular theoretical understanding of inflation, and scientists have scant observational or experimental evidence to validate *any* specific inflationary model at this time.

Level III—The Quantum Mechanical Multiverse

In *Back to the Future*, Marty McFly travels through time, back to 1955 when his parents first met. The time machine, a plutonium-powered Delorean, requires 1.21 gigawatts to operate the flux capacitor—the device that makes Marty's time travel possible.

As he interacts with his teenaged parents, Marty disrupts the sequence of events leading to their marriage, thus putting his very existence in jeopardy. Eventually, he and his friend Doc Brown, inventor of the flux capacitor, get Marty's parents together. Because of his interference in the past, when Marty returns to his proper time he finds things at home noticeably improved.

The movie implies that Marty moves back and forth on a single timeline where his familiar world no longer exists. Today, some interpretations of quantum mechanics argue that Marty's old known time-line, as well as the new one resulting from his interference, now both exist! In fact, these interpretations posit that every quantum event, whether initiated by conscious beings or occurring between atoms, produces new universes. A little background helps illustrate why this would be so.

At the start of the 1900s, the foundations of quantum mechanics were just being laid. According to prevailing scientific models at that time, no limit existed on scientists' ability to measure any quantity. Though technology placed practical restrictions on such measurements, no fundamental barrier existed. Over the past century, many beautiful experiments have confirmed the validity and necessity of quantum mechanics to describe nature. These same experiments have also changed some preconceived notions of nature's seemingly obvious characteristics.

At the same time, quantum mechanics has imposed some stringent limits on scientists' abilities to measure certain quantities. For example, determining the position of a football using a measuring stick marked in one inch intervals gives an answer in inches. Because the ruler contains no finer markings, an uncertainty of roughly half-an-inch either way exists. A ruler with finer markings permits finer measurements.

Determining the velocity of the football presents a similar situation. According to classical mechanics, both the position and velocity of the ball can be determined to an arbitrarily small uncertainty by using better and better measuring devices.

In contrast, quantum mechanics declares that the product of the position and velocity uncertainties must always be greater than some minimum value.[20] In fact, this means an *exact* measure of the ball's position renders the ball's velocity completely unknowable! A similar relationship exists between energy and time. For large objects people encounter everyday, the limits on simultaneously measuring position and velocity are not particularly restrictive. However, such limits significantly influence experiments involving protons, electrons, or other small particles.

Another difference between the classical world and the quantum mechanical realm relates to the available configurations a system can assume. Classically, any quantity (like distance or energy) divides into infinitely small amounts. Quantum mechanics dictates that these quantities change by discrete amounts.

The net result of these two quantum mechanical effects—the inherent uncertainty in measuring certain pairs of quantities and the discrete nature of possible states—is that scientists can calculate results of quantum mechanical experiments only in terms of probabilities. When calculating these probabilities, scientists must account for every possible outcome of a given experiment.

One interpretation of the reality underlying quantum mechanics is that whenever a quantum event appears to have many outcomes with different probabilities, each outcome *actually occurs*. The futures that follow each outcome represent new branch "universes" that never again interact. Stated more simply, (and illustrated in figure 5, page 23) when Marty McFly interacts with his parents in 1955, he unknowingly produces a new future that never again intersects the original

Figure 5. Level III Multiverse
©Aaron Garcia

timeline. But both timelines continue to exist. This cinematic example of the collection of all past and future timelines represents the Level III multiverse.[21]

Evidence Supporting Level III

According to everyday experience, objects have definite locations and velocities. Furthermore, these objects obey rules that allow scientists to use measurements made in the past to predict with certainty their future positions and velocities. However, this "classical" picture of the world only approximates the more fundamental quantum mechanical nature of the universe. And the world of quantum mechanics is strange.

A thought experiment by Erwin Schrödinger, an early scientist studying quantum mechanics, demonstrates the strangeness. Imagine a cat confined to a box. A scientist then puts a radioactive material inside the box. When an atom of the radioactive material decays, it registers on a Geiger counter, causing the release of a poison that kills the cat. At any given time, there is some probability that the atom has decayed and some probability that it has not. All this makes sense in a classical picture.

According to quantum mechanics, the atom exists in a state described as a combination of its original state and its decayed state. While that may make sense for the atom, the condition of the cat depends on the state of the atom. The cat thus exists in a combination of a live state and a dead state!

Without question, the mathematical formulas and operations describing quantum mechanics accurately predict the results scientists measure when performing experiments. However, since its development in the early 1900s, the proper interpretation of quantum mechanics has generated great debate. Of particular interest is the actual mechanism that takes the bizarre workings of the quantum world (like the cat being both alive and dead at the same time) into the concrete results of the classical world.

While the debate over the proper interpretation of quantum mechanics continues, two aspects of this debate support the ideas behind the Level III multiverse. Scientists argue that the fundamental equations of physics follow the rule that the probabilities for all possible states add up to one—a condition called "unitarity." Unitary equations remove any of the quantum randomness (and the consequent unknownness or uncertainty) that trouble many physicists,[22] but at the expense of requiring that all the possible states actually exist.

Over the last few decades, scientists have articulated another idea called "decoherence" as a way to resolve the difficulties in transitioning from the quantum world to the classical world. Decoherence argues that interactions of a quantum mechanical system with the environment shield the observer from any of the quantum weirdness. But, if decoherence is true, it also implies the actual existence of all possible quantum states.

The ideas of unitarity and decoherence provide philosophical support for the Level III multiverse, which gained prominence through the work of Hugh Everett, a graduate student of the late John Wheeler. While research into the Level III multiverse remains an area of great scientific interest, the remainder of this booklet does not require a detailed understanding of it. (Max Tegmark's article "Parallel Universes" also provides a good starting reference for those seeking a deeper understanding of this particular model.[23])

Level IV Multiverse—Everything's Possible

According to a growing number of scientists, the existence of our universe, even if it encompasses other levels of multiverse, still raises the question: Why these laws of physics and not others? An answer becomes clear—*if* universes with every mathematically consistent set of physical laws actually exist. In essence, this Level IV multiverse consists of an ensemble of every conceivable universe. Thus, no additional multiverse levels can exist.

The degree of speculation increases with each multiverse level, making the Level IV multiverse the most speculative by far. In fact, scientists have no observational evidence to address the existence (or non-existence) of the Level IV multiverse. (See figure 6, pages 28–29 for a summary of the four main types of multiverse models.)

OTHER MULTIVERSE MODELS

The previous discussion outlines the most popular multiverse models at each level. However, scientific literature contains a number of other important models that demonstrate specific variations of the four main models that scientists have envisioned.

Endless Cycles

One model, proposed years ago but recently fleshed out by Paul Steinhardt and Neil Turok, employs only a Level I multiverse.[24] Instead of inflation generating a bunch of bubble universes, only one universe exists that undergoes cycles of expansion and contraction. Each new cycle represents a new Level I multiverse (spatially infinite and geometrically flat) governed by physical laws that might vary slightly from cycle to cycle. After accounting for all the cycles, the cyclical multiverse produces a diversity of universes similar to the Level II multiverse.

This model may seem like the failed oscillating universe model popular in the 1960s and 1970s. However, this new model circumvents many of the shortcomings of the oscillating model by postulating alternative physics. Currently, the model does not specify the mechanism that causes the cycling.

Growing Black Holes

Lee Smolin proposed another version of the Level II multiverse wherein black holes, instead of inflation, provide the universe-generating mechanism.[25] In his version, when a black hole forms it causes a rupture in the space-time fabric. Smolin's model suggests that subsequent reconnecting of the rip leads to the formation of a new universe. Like the cyclical model above, this model also posits that the laws of physics governing the new universe will differ slightly from those in the universe where the original black hole formed. This mechanism would provide a naturalistic explanation for the existence of a universe capable of supporting life, assuming the same laws of physics that permit life also produce a universe with a requisite number of black holes. According to this model, those universes with abundant black holes also spawn the most daughter universes. So the number of habitable universes would grow with time.

Looking Back in Time

Stephen Hawking and Thomas Hertog offer a markedly different way of explaining the universe.[26] Instead of starting with a well-defined initial condition for the universe and tracking a single history up to the present time, Hawking and Hertog start with the universe at later times, as measured by astronomers, and work backwards. While the familiar universe traces a unique history back to the first second, before the first second, multiple different histories would have influenced the future state of our universe. In other words, Hawking and Hertog propose that in order to reproduce how this universe appears after the first second, multiple different parallel universes (or histories) existed before the first second, each of which influenced how this universe subsequently developed. These multiple histories correspond to a multiverse similar to the Level III multiverse.

Such multiverse variants reflect researchers' difficulty in understanding the earliest moments of the universe. The scant evidence directly addressing the moment immediately after the big bang makes it difficult to determine which theoretical picture of the universe actually corresponds to reality.

In fact, a major challenge in developing multiverse models is making them sufficiently detailed for testability. Scientists rely on measurements to determine a model's viability. At this point, no observational evidence exists that strongly favors any of the models beyond a Level I multiverse.

MORE ON LEVELS I AND II

Most multiverse discussions revolve around the Level I and Level II multiverses. Because of their reliance on inflation and string theory, these two models have the most promising ties to experimental evidence and provide naturalists with (arguably) their strongest response to the fine-tuning observed in our universe.

Beyond solving the horizon, flatness, and monopole problems, inflation makes other predictions that astronomers and cosmologists seek to verify. In particular, inflation stamps its signature on the CMB radiation in ways detectable by the most recent experiments (and in ways that future experiments should detect in even more detail). Thus far, astronomers have found all the expected signatures they have the capacity to detect.[27] However, while evidence strongly indicates an inflationary period in the universe, inflation does not inherently support anything beyond a Level I multiverse.

The tie-in to the Level II multiverse arises from attempts to provide a theoretical understanding of the processes driving inflation. Currently, the only theoretical understandings of inflation consistent with the observable universe predict both the existence of other bubble universes (which presumably populate the Level II multiverse) and a spatially infinite Level I multiverse within our bubble universe.

Originally, string theorists hoped that as they searched for solutions to the equations of string theory only one solution would emerge (and therefore only one possible universe, one that looks like ours). Today that appears unlikely, as the number of possible solutions (each representing a possible universe) to the equations of string theory is enormous—approximately 10^{500}. For comparison, only 10^{80} protons exist in the observable universe.

Unwilling to be discouraged by such a development, some theorists treated this number as a welcome finding. If inflation produces a large number of bubble universes (the Level II multiverse), string theory might describe the potentially enormous and varied physical landscapes (including different laws of physics) of those universes within. The theoretical basis for the Level II multiverse provided by inflation and string theory, as well as the possible capacity of this particular model to address the issue of cosmic fine-tuning, draws many scientists into the multiverse camp.

LEVEL I

Features:
- Other regions the size of our observable universe
- Governed by same laws of physics and fundamental constants

Location:
- Beyond the edge of the observable universe

Support:
- Inflation means that space likely does not end at the edge of the observable universe

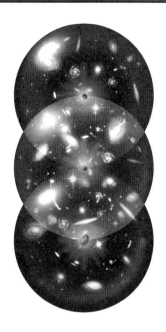

LEVEL II

Features:
- Other universes inside bubbles where inflation ceased
- Governed by different laws of physics and fundamental constants

Location:
- Infinitely beyond the edge of the observable universe

Support:
- Some theories of inflation predict other universes
- String theory indicates that many different arrangements of the laws of physics and constants exist

Figure 6. Different Multiverse Levels ©Aaron Garcia

LEVEL III

Features:
- Other universes "generated" by the different possible outcomes of each quantum mechanical event
- Diversity of environments is the same as Level I and Level II when combined

Location:
- Different regions in a mathematically defined space

Support:
- Interpretations of quantum mechanics that involve decoherence and unitarity

LEVEL IV

Features:
- Every mathematically consistent reality exists

Location:
- Somewhere else in "math space"

Support:
- Would describe all possible realities

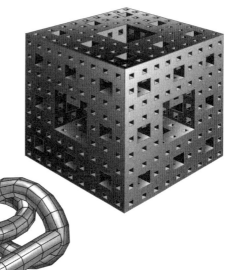

Figure 6. Different Multiverse Levels ©Aaron Garcia

APOLOGETIC IMPACT OF THE MULTIVERSE

Understanding the various multiverse models provides the background for addressing the issue of how the multiverse impacts some of the most important arguments for God's existence and his involvement in the universe. In order for a *strictly naturalistic* multiverse model to provide an adequate explanation for the universe and our existence, it must meet a number of criteria.

FIVE REQUIREMENTS

First, any naturalistic multiverse model must be self-contained. Christianity argues that the universe has a beginning (and thus a Beginner) and that the universe exhibits design for human habitability. A naturalistic model cannot exhibit a beginning or true design because each requires an external agent—a Beginner or a Designer. Thus, any proposed multiverse model must explain the apparent design acknowledged by the scientific community without allowing any aspect of the model to reflect *actual* design or fine-tuning.

Second, any successful multiverse model must account for all relevant observations and data. In other words, any proposed multiverse model must naturally produce a region that looks like the observable universe. In addition, since any multiverse would, by definition, lie forever beyond the reach of observation, any multiverse model must make predictions about what scientists will detect in our observable universe. Otherwise, no scientific tests can verify or falsify the model.

Third, the model must provide a mechanism that produces a sufficient variety (for probability's sake) of universes. According to probability theory, a monkey typing away for an enormously long time will eventually reproduce the complete works of William Shakespeare. However, the argument is true only if the keyboard contains all the letters of the alphabet. With a keyboard of vowels only, the monkey will never produce any readable work regardless of how long the typing continues. Similarly, unless a multiverse model produces a sufficient variety of universes, it cannot explain the fine-tuning observed in the known universe—specifically in the laws of physics, the fundamental constants, the characteristics of the Milky Way Galaxy, and the features of the solar system's Sun, Earth–Moon system, other planets and moons, and more.

Fourth, our universe must be one of the possible universes in the multiverse model. Otherwise the model is like a keyboard with no 'e.'

Fifth, for a naturalistic multiverse model, life must be solely physical. Although this requirement flows from the first, it bears separate mention to highlight its importance. All naturalistic multiverse models I have encountered so far implicitly make the assumption that life is completely physical. However, if human life possesses a nonphysical component, such as a soul or spirit, then no amount of tweaking the laws of physics and rearranging the stuff of the universe will produce a human being.

While this list of requirements may seem impossibly daunting, a number of scientists have nevertheless attempted to build completely naturalistic multiverse models. So let's evaluate how well multiverse models fare when examined against this standard. We begin by focusing on two important arguments for a Creator and by assessing the available scientific evidence for design. For reasons that will become clear later, some philosophical issues are involved as well.

THE COSMOLOGICAL ARGUMENT

The cosmological arguments provide one of the most compelling pieces of evidence for the existence of a Creator. From a scientific perspective, the kalam version of the cosmological argument is most relevant. The kalam argument is typically articulated this way:

1. Whatever begins to exist has a cause.
2. The universe began to exist.
3. Therefore, the universe has a cause.

In philosophical terms, the cosmological argument is a syllogism. The major premise and minor premise (items 1 and 2, respectively) are used to draw the conclusion (item 3). In this instance, the major premise is largely uncontroversial.[28] An abundance of scientific evidence supports the minor premise.

Big bang cosmology provides the umbrella for evidence of the universe's beginning. Extensive verification of general relativity coupled with the measured expansion of the universe point to a singular beginning of the universe.

The first of the space-time theorems of general relativity derived by Stephen Hawking, Roger Penrose and George Ellis provides further corroboration that the universe has a beginning.[29] Detailed measurements of the CMB also point to a beginning and numerous techniques give similar dates for the age of the universe. Readers interested in more details of this evidence should see *The Creator and the Cosmos* by Hugh Ross.[30]

Big bang cosmology buttresses the minor premise, which consequently strengthens confidence in the conclusion that the universe was supernaturally caused. Therefore, the main concern regarding the multiverse is how it impacts the question of the universe's beginning.

Does the Multiverse Have a Beginning?

Different multiverse models answer this origin question differently. In its usual form, a Level I multiverse still starts with a big bang. Remember, the age and expansion rate of the universe determine the size of the observable universe. As long as the total universe is larger than our observable universe, a Level I multiverse exists. However, big bang cosmology still asserts a beginning for the Level I multiverse.

In the Level II multiverse, the situation is more complicated. Within this model, big bang cosmology still governs our universe since its beginning, but other universes beyond ours have different beginnings. According to the most accepted theoretical models of inflation, new bubble universes continue forming forever into the future. If inflation produces universes perpetually into the future, some scientists think it might have been doing so forever into the past as well. If so, the inflationary multiverse would be truly eternal. According to Alan Guth, the appeal of an eternal cosmos "frees us from all questions about how the universe was created, or what existed before the universe was created."[31]

In the context of big bang cosmology, the space-time theorems of general relativity conclusively settled the question in favor of a beginning. The strength of the space-time theorems rests on the validity of general relativity. While most scientists expect that general relativity does not adequately describe gravity in the earliest moments after the big bang, Guth and two collaborators developed a theorem that does not depend on the validity of general relativity. The theorem (known as the BVG theorem after its developers, Arvind Borde, Alexander Vilenkin, and Alan Guth) demonstrates that *any* cosmos that expands on average (like the inflationary multiverse) *must have a beginning* in the finite past.[32] Ironically, the implications of the most popular Level II multiverse actually strengthen the cosmological argument by making it more robust.

THE TELEOLOGICAL ARGUMENT

Alongside the cosmological argument, the teleological argument also provides strong evidence for the reality of a Creator/Designer. The argument simply states that any true design requires a designer. Therefore, if the universe exhibits true design, then a Designer exists.

Although alien civilizations permeate science fiction literature and film, a wealth of scientific evidence discovered over the last half-century highlights Earth's unique capacity to support advanced and human life. Carbon-based life places severe restrictions on the laws of physics and composition of the universe. Even with the proper physics, the evidence indicates that life wouldn't be possible apart from the right kind of planet with the just-right moon and just-right planetary partners orbiting a just-right star in a just-right galaxy.[33]

In addition, only a relatively narrow time-window in this universe permits the existence of such a planet.[34] Assuming the operation of strictly natural processes, all these constraints translate to an extremely low probability for advanced life.

Yet we exist.

Given the extreme improbabilities against it, our existence demands an explanation. Christians throughout history have argued that the work of a supernatural Creator provides the best account of the universe's capacity to support life. From the simplest bacteria to complex humans, all life traces its origins to divine creative acts. In contrast, strict naturalists have traditionally argued that the physical universe is the ultimate reality and all it contains arises solely from impersonal laws.

The central issue of the teleological argument is this question: Does this universe exhibit purpose? Does it look the way scientists expect it to look or does it look somehow odd or unnatural? Abundant evidence indicates that the features of the observable universe are "skewed," or fine-tuned, to support life.[35] The extreme improbability that all the requirements for life would converge by natural processes alone argues for the involvement of a Creator. Proponents of naturalism have attempted to explain the appearance of design as the result of a huge "selection effect."

What is a Selection Effect?

Various activities require different equipment and different techniques. Take fishing for example. Imagine using a lure so big that only bass with a two-inch-wide (or wider) mouth could grab it. Even if you were to catch a whole mess of bass with that lure, you would be wrong to conclude that the lake contained no bass with mouths smaller than two inches. Equipment must be accounted for, or else the wrong conclusions will be drawn. The choice of lures *selected* bass with mouths larger than two inches.

Applying this example to scientific investigations means that when drawing conclusions, scientists must properly account for the selection effects of the equipment they use. Scientists are aware that their equipment selects what data they measure and they work to minimize the impact equipment makes on their observations.

However, a large selection effect occurs when scientists try to understand fundamental questions about the universe—in particular, why the universe supports life. The laws of physics manifest exacting values among a vast range of possibilities making it possible for the universe to support life. Earth exhibits numerous characteristics necessary to life that, if changed slightly, would render Earth uninhabitable. Why do scientists observe this highly improbable set of circumstances given the vast number of other possibilities?

The one final variable required for an answer is the creature asking the question. Without humans (or some other similarly self-aware being) around, questions regarding the nature of the universe would never be asked. Our very existence requires that we observe a life-supporting universe. Thus, many naturalists argue that the fine-tuned appearance of our universe is not unexpected or unnatural since we humans represent a selection effect. The weak anthropic principle (WAP) embodies this line of reasoning. One popular formulation of the WAP says:

> The observed values of all physical and cosmological quantities are not equally probable but they take on values restricted by the requirement that there exist sites where carbon-based life can evolve and by the requirement that the Universe be old enough for it to have already done so.[36]

While our existence does bear undeniable testimony to the fact that the observable universe supports sentient life, the WAP falls short as a naturalistic explanation of the universe's life-support capacity. Richard Swinburne developed an analogy specifically illustrating the fallacy involved in this explanation. Swinburne lays out the following scenario:

> On a certain occasion the firing squad aim their rifles at the prisoner to be executed. There are twelve expert marksmen in the firing squad, and they fire twelve rounds each. However, on this occasion all 144 shots miss. The prisoner laughs and comments that the event is not something requiring any explanation because if the marksmen had not missed, he would not be here to observe them having done so.[37]

Notice the parallel between the prisoner's declaring that nothing about his survival needs explanation and the naturalist's using the WAP as an ultimate explanation for the universe's habitability. The prisoner notices that he lives only if the expert marksmen all miss him with every shot. Humans observe a habitable universe only if a universe capable of supporting complex life supports them. However, Swinburne continues by noting:

> But of course the prisoner's comment is absurd; the marksmen all having missed is indeed something requiring explanation; and so too is what goes with it—the prisoner's being alive to observe it.[38]

Not one scientist I know would be satisfied by the prisoner's explanation. In fact, I would expect many discussions trying to understand how such an unlikely event occurred. Were blanks used instead of bullets? Were the gun sights intentionally misaligned? Did the marksmen conspire to spare the prisoner? Other options come to mind. But all reasonable explanations involve the action of an intelligent being.

Ultimately, the weak anthropic principle leaves unresolved the issue of why these laws of physics, laws that permit complex life, govern our universe. Among all the seemingly possible laws, only a tiny minority would permit life. Why, given only one shot, did the universe end up with a set of laws that permit life? The multiverse attempts to resolve the deficiencies of the WAP explanation by positing the existence of a great number of universes from which life can select.

THE EVIDENCE FOR FINE-TUNING

The evidence for fine-tuning divides into two different categories: "environmental" and "fundamental." The environmental category includes quantities that appear fine-tuned but vary with location or time in the universe. Some examples include the planet/moon size and composition, star type, galaxy type and size, etc. The latter category includes quantities that are set at the earliest moments in creation and either remain constant or change according to strictly defined laws. Examples of fundamental fine-tuned quantities include the strengths of the fundamental forces, the mass density of the universe, the expansion rate, and the dimensionality.

Environmental

Using environmental fine-tuning evidence to argue for a supernatural Creator ultimately boils down to a probability argument. Given the laws of physics and fundamental constants of the observable universe, how "common" are planets capable of supporting complex life like human beings? A vast body of research establishes that the chemical complexity based on the element carbon dwarfs the complexity available from any other element. Since physical life requires a high degree of chemical complexity, the requirements should be restricted to those dictated by carbon-based life.

What are the chances that an Earth-like planet gets such a large moon in order to stabilize its rotation axis and provide tidal interactions that replenish nutrients on the continental shelves? What are the chances that a star forms close enough to the supernovae that enrich an Earth-like planet with sufficient radioactive elements to drive plate tectonics for billions of years? What are the odds that a star resides in a spiral galaxy where star formation continues late enough to incorporate the heavy elements after earlier supernovae enrich the interstellar medium?

As astronomers, geologists, physicists, and other scientists develop a deeper understanding of the processes responsible for generating galaxies, stars, and planets, the continually accumulating evidence drives these probabilities lower and lower. Even with a billion trillion stars available in the observable universe, the probabilities stack up against finding even one planet capable of hosting advanced life. Additionally, given an Earth-like planet, the probabilities of all the steps leading from nonliving, inorganic molecules to the first life-forms reduce the chances even further.

Fundamental

In contrast with most of the environmental fine-tuning parameters, scientists struggle to assign probabilities to the fundamental fine-tuning parameters. For example, in the context of environmental fine-tuning, the laws of physics constrain the range and distribution of characteristics for galaxies, stars, and planets. However, few such constraints exist for the laws of physics themselves, and their associated fundamental constants.

While many scientists hope to find the ultimate unified "theory of everything" (TOE) that yields these constraints, prospects for that hope appear dim. In fact, a string of theoretical evidence indicates that a vast multitude of possible laws and physical constants might exist.

DOES THE MULTIVERSE NATURALLY EXPLAIN THE FINE-TUNING?

So how does a naturalistic multiverse attempt to explain the environmental and fundamental fine-tuning scientists see? In order to argue that fine-tuning results from a selection effect (i.e., the observable universe is amenable to life because life requires such a universe) the universe must be sufficiently large to counteract the enormous improbabilities indicated by the degree of fine-tuning. Each level of the multiverse addresses these probabilities in different ways.

Even the Level I multiverse impacts the environmental fine-tuning argument. While the minimum size of the Level I multiverse exceeds a thousand times the size of the observable universe, scientists expect it to be much larger. In fact, the simplest theories for how inflation operates argue for a spatially infinite universe.[39] Even if it is not spatially infinite, the total universe could potentially be many orders of magnitude larger than the observable universe.

Imagine sitting down to a game of poker. The chance of drawing a royal flush in spades from a standard deck of fifty-two cards is about one in 2.5 million.[40] However, drawing five cards 10 billion times virtually assures that a person will draw at least one royal flush in spades, in fact, many more than one.

Similarly, scientists can calculate the total possible states and histories of the matter, energy, space, and time included in the observable universe. While an incredibly large number, the total number of possible states and histories of the observable universe is finite. Thus, if a large enough number of regions the size of the observable universe exist in the Level I multiverse, *and* if the unobserved regions sample a sufficiently diverse set of initial conditions, the state corresponding to ours would surely arise. However, the exacting conditions and events required for life mean the vast majority of the Level I multiverse simply cannot contain life.

Of necessity, for life to exist scientists must observe an environment wherein all the conditions for life are met. Thus, a large enough Level I multiverse might allow a naturalistic explanation for why scientists observe the fine-tuned appearance of our local *environment*. However, regardless of the total universe's spatial extent, no life exists unless the *fundamental* laws of physics and associated constants assume a form that permits life. Among all the possible forms of the physical laws and all the permissible values for the fundamental constants, an extremely small range allows life. Since a Level I multiverse samples only one of the many possible laws of physics and associated constants, this *fundamental* fine-tuning remains, even in a spatially infinite universe.

The Level II multiverse argues that inflation actually produces universes exhibiting all the possible laws of physics. Admittedly, the Level II multiverse is more speculative than the Level I multiverse. However, *if* the Level II multiverse exists, and *if* the laws and constants vary among the bubble universes, and *if* those laws and constants sample all possible values of the fine-tuned traits (three big *ifs*), then the Level II multiverse coupled with the WAP provides an answer to the apparent fine-tuning of our observable universe. The actuality of such a multiverse remedies the otherwise insufficient explanation supplied by the WAP alone because it provides a realized existence from which life selects (again, assuming life is completely physical and arises by purely physical processes). Of all the different bubble universes, life (such as humans) will only observe a bubble capable of supporting it. The important issue becomes this: Does the required Level II multiverse actually exist? Currently, scant physical evidence addresses this question one way or the other.

Another Big IF

Most scientists believe that the enormous temperatures and pressures in the early universe caused all the fundamental forces—gravity, electromagnetism, and the strong and weak nuclear forces—to appear (initially) as one unified force. As the universe cooled, most TOEs feature transitions where this unified force separated into the distinct forces seen today. Some scientists hypothesize that the TOE may permit different regions of the Level I multiverse to cool in such a way that causes the forces to separate with different strengths. If this proves true, then a spatially infinite Level I multiverse together with the WAP may explain both the environmental and fundamental fine-tuning seen in our observable universe.

This version of the Level I multiverse is testable. If and when astronomers can make sufficiently accurate measurements on the values of the fundamental forces and constants in the most distant parts of the universe, they may be able to detect any differences in those values compared to measurements made near Earth.

Already, the limits on possible variations are extremely small.[41]

Although admittedly speculative, scientists can conceive of universes with different physical laws based on large (but reasonable) extrapolations from currently accepted theories. If the number of universes is sufficiently large, a wide range of possible configurations for matter and energy would be expected to occur in these hypothetical universes. Thus, inflationary cosmology might provide a class of models with sufficient diversity to account for both the environmental fine-tuning and the fundamental fine-tuning. However, other problems—both scientific and philosophical—arise for strictly naturalistic multiverse models.

SCIENTIFIC OBJECTIONS TO THE MULTIVERSE

FLAT GEOMETRY

Most multiverse models rely heavily on inflation. It solves the horizon, flatness, and monopole problems, and a growing body of physical evidence indicates that inflation did indeed occur. Inflation's effects, in turn, provide the (only) significant pieces of theoretical evidence supporting the possibility of a Level II multiverse, and researchers anticipate that by measuring these effects, their models could be validated. The type of inflation required by spatially infinite Level I multiverses and Level II multiverse models would leave a distinct signature on the universe's geometry. In particular, multiverse-producing inflation would lead to an open observable universe (although not all open universe models are multiverse models).[42]

The connection between openness and flatness is this: cosmologists define the geometry of the universe in terms of a curvature density. Positive curvature density corresponds to open, negative corresponds to closed, and zero corresponds to flat. (See "What is Flat?" and "Defining the Measure of the Universe's Geometry" sidebars on pages 11 and 40, respectively.) CMB measurements, combined with Type Ia supernovae data and large-scale structure measurements, give a curvature density larger than -0.0170 but smaller than 0.0068.[43] Thus, geometry measurements favor a closed universe (most of the allowed range for the curvature density is negative) although the error bars also allow for both a flat or open universe.

While future measurements might strengthen the case for a closed geometry, most theoretical descriptions of inflation produce extremely flat universes. On this basis, scientists expect that future measurements will show the curvature density closer and closer to zero (with steadily decreasing error bars), rather than measure a positive curvature density (meaning an open universe) required by a Level II multiverse. In other words, if the universe is flat, as many cosmologists expect, the error bars on the measured curvature density will always permit an open, closed, or flat geometry.

DEFINING THE MEASURE OF THE UNIVERSE'S GEOMETRY

Until the mid-1990s, the only known component of the universe that affected its expansion was mass/energy. Consequently, the future expansion of the universe corresponded with its geometry. In an open universe, the cosmos expands forever although gravity slows the expansion. In a closed universe gravity halts the expansion and causes the universe to collapse back on itself. A flat universe represents the critical point between the open and closed universes—gravity slows the expansion to zero in the infinite future.[44] The CMB radiation provides the most precise measurement of the universe's geometry. A common parameter used to describe the geometry is the total density of the universe.

Scientists call the density required to produce a flat universe the critical density. However, the discovery and confirmation of space-energy density over the last decade complicate the picture. The existence of space-energy density means that the total mass/energy density no longer determines the future expansion. In other words, even in a universe with more than the critical density, the space-energy density can cause it to expand forever. Consequently, astronomers defined a new term to quantify the geometry of the universe: the curvature density. Negative curvature density corresponds to closed, positive corresponds to open, and zero corresponds to flat.

SPHERICAL HARMONICS

An additional piece of evidence derived from the CMB also argues against a spatially infinite Level I multiverse. The ripples first observed by COBE, then focused by the Wilkinson Microwave Anisotropy Probe (WMAP), appear as bumps, dots, and smudges on a map of the sky. In one context, such features resemble musical notes and harmonics.

A scientist with the proper tools could break down a musical score into various notes and harmonics and use that information to calculate how frequently the composer used each harmonic. Similarly, scientists analyze the ripples of the CMB to determine the amount of power the CMB exhibits in each "spherical harmonic." Instead of a musical frequency, the spherical harmonics correspond to a length scale—higher harmonics represent smaller length scales and vice versa.

In a flat, spatially infinite universe, each spherical harmonic would exhibit the same amount of power. However, a finite-sized universe limits the power on larger scales and, therefore, in lower harmonics. The lowest harmonic in the CMB measures significantly below what a spatially infinite universe predicts. This finding provides another indicator of a spatially finite universe.[45]

The geometry of the observable universe and the smallest spherical harmonics from the CMB represent the only pieces of experimental or observational evidence directly addressing the reality of multiverses. All indications from currently available data seem to militate against a multiverse that would explain all the fine-tuning for life seen in this universe. It would be a gross overstatement to say this evidence completely rules out inflation-generated, spatially infinite multiverses. Rather, more data and additional tests are required to determine the validity of the inflationary Level II multiverse.

MODEL BUILDING BIASES

As mentioned previously, the simplest theoretical understandings of inflation that come close to matching astronomers' observations of the universe predict a Level II universe filled with spatially infinite Level I multiverses (a prediction currently at odds with measured values). However, it should be noted that philosophical opposition to the idea of a supernatural Agency as the cause of the universe and its fine-tuning for life strongly motivates many scientists to seek inflation models such as those currently popular. In reflecting on the idea that an inflation-generated Level II multiverse actually exists, cosmologist George Ellis stated:

The multiverse situation seems to fit St. Paul's description: "Faith is the substance of things hoped for, the evidence of things not seen." In this case, it is faith that enormous extrapolations from tested physics are correct; *hope that correct hints as to the way things really are have been identified from all the possibilities*, and that the present marginal evidence to the contrary will go away.[46] (italics added)

Multiverse advocates face many more hurdles than the scientific ones addressed in these pages. The remaining challenges reflect a more philosophical bent.

PHILOSOPHICAL DIFFICULTIES

ABSURD INFINITIES

As RTB's creation model argues, big bang cosmology provides powerful corroboration of the biblical creation scenario. That all the space, time, matter, and energy of the universe share a common origin strongly contends for a supernatural Creator. Some scientists reject this conclusion because big bang cosmologies, when traced to the earliest moment, typically lead to an infinitely dense universe. To most scientists, infinities signify areas where a model breaks down indicating the need for a new, more comprehensive model that removes the infinities. However, many scientists seem to embrace the spatial infinity of the Level I multiverse predicted by most inflationary cosmologies.

In the context of inflationary theory, the spatially infinite region inside a bubble universe arises from a future time infinity outside the bubble. In other words, when viewing the bubble that contains our universe from the outside über-space, the bubble grows forever into the future. This future time infinity outside the bubble becomes an infinite space inside the bubble.[47]

A number of philosophical objections may be raised against anything growing from finite to infinite (as the future time infinity must to produce a spatially infinite Level I multiverse). For example, consider the orbits of Earth and Jupiter. Earth orbits the Sun almost twelve times for each orbit Jupiter makes. Thus, after any finite time the ratio of Earth orbits to Jupiter orbits is twelve to one. However, after an infinite time, each planet will complete an infinite number of orbits, and, according to mathematical rules for infinities, each planet has thus completed an identical number of orbits!

Similarly, consider a hotel with an infinite number of rooms—each room containing a guest. Ten more people arrive and request rooms. The hotel owner instructs each guest to move to the room with a door numbered ten larger than that of his or her current room, thus freeing up rooms one through ten.

Now imagine an infinitely large party comes, requesting rooms. "No problem," declares the owner. He simply asks each guest to move to the room with a number double that of his or her current room. Now the infinite set of odd numbered rooms contains no guests and can accommodate the infinite party that just arrived.

These examples highlight the bizarre situations that can arise when working with infinities. Mathematically, well-defined rules exist for dealing with such circumstances. However, problems surface when applying these rules to a physical world. At the very minimum, allowing for actual infinities requires rewriting our intuitive notions of addition, subtraction, multiplication, division, logic, and comparison. The physical world may force that change, but it should not be undertaken casually—certainly not without compelling physical evidence.

WILL THE REAL ME STEP FORWARD?

Recall the earlier description regarding the probability of drawing a royal flush in spades from a deck of cards. Although the chance that any given hand will contain this royal flush is one in 2.5 million, ten billion draws virtually ensures a large number of such hands. The same ten billion draws also ensure many hands in every possible five-card combination. Simply based on the known probabilities for each possible five-card combination, a person can easily calculate how many of the ten billion hands contain each of those combinations. Applying the same reasoning to the spatially infinite Level I multiverse hints at a startling conclusion.

The two examples given below assume that all life, including human life, is purely physical. Recall, a naturalistic multiverse demands this condition.

Identity

Given the size of the observable universe, only a finite number of states and histories are conceivable (though that number is extremely large). If every one of those states and histories actually exists somewhere in the Level I multiverse, a bizarre situation presents itself. The observable universe corresponds to one of those histories—assuming a completely physical basis for life. However, in other regions of a possible multiverse, *you* might have written this booklet. In another history, you wrote it—in Swahili. In another, you include a recipe for homemade chili in the back of the booklet. In still another, it did not get written at all.

If we look just at those regions where you wrote the booklet, each has its own history. In some of those regions you rewrite the whole booklet 500 times. In others, you start but don't finish. In other regions, the booklet is banned, and you are blacklisted as a dangerous, radical author. In some the booklet is too small to contain all your ideas, and it becomes a 1,000-page tome. Nothing in the laws of physics would prohibit *any* of these scenarios. So each history must be realized somewhere in the multiverse. In fact, the spatially infinite multiverse realizes each physical history an infinite number of times! But which one is the real "you?"

Justice and Free Will

Such a situation would raise troubling issues regarding the universality of accepted human values and standards of right and wrong. For example, every known human society and culture sees premeditated murder as worthy of judgment. Consider this scenario: someone in the observable universe commits murder and receives an appropriate sentence, but in other regions of such a multiverse, the same murderer escapes judgment by eluding authorities, breaking out of jail before (or after sentencing), or being acquitted by the jury. If a killer can get away with murder in some regions and not in others, is justice real? In the observable universe, society might exercise capital punishment and execute the murderer, while in other multiverse regions the would-be murderer changes his mind or fails in the attempt. Is justice served?

The possible existence of the multiverse's multitude of histories would dramatically impact our notion of justice and free will. Are criminals truly held accountable for their actions in the observable universe when they don't actually commit those actions in some other regions of the multiverse? If all conceivable histories actually occur somewhere in the proposed multiverse, then in some regions a person commits the murder and in other regions the same person doesn't. In a strictly natural multiverse, purely physical processes dictate which outcome occurs in which region. This begs the question, "Does the person have real choice in committing or not committing the murder?"

These scenarios highlight fundamental philosophical and moral challenges to reconciling a naturalistic multiverse response with universally accepted human values. At the core of this challenge lie these questions: Of the essentially identical beings bearing my name and likeness scattered throughout this proposed multiverse, which is the real me? What's more, do I really have any choice in, or any responsibility for, what I do? These questions point to some of the alarming consequences of a spatially infinite (or sufficiently large) Level I multiverse, issues that a naturalist must address. Either the principles of identity, justice, and free will are fundamentally illusory or something militates against humanity's existence throughout the multiverse.

From a Christian perspective, human life is not purely physical and does not arise by strictly natural processes. Instead, human life results from a direct creative act by God. Thus, human life exists only where God created it even if the multiverse proves true.

IS HUMAN LIFE TYPICAL?

All the evidence marshaled in support of fine-tuning argues for the rarity of advanced life in any limited portion of the universe—a fact readily acknowledged by many scientists. In fact, most research focuses on reconciling the existence of human life with its low probability. Thus, by itself, the weak anthropic principle fails to address the central question of life's existence.

In contrast, advanced life must abound in any naturalistic multiverse scenario (because, according to naturalism, life is purely physical and arises spontaneously). Consequently, the naturalist must answer a different question: What is the likelihood that of all the possible life-forms capable of observing the universe, it is we human beings on a 4.5 billion-year-old rocky planet orbiting a third generation star in an old, spiral galaxy in a 13.7-billion-year-old universe who would be those observers? At least two other options represent far more likely possibilities.

Simulating the Universe

The blockbuster trilogy series *The Matrix* revolves around the premise that the world experienced by human beings originates from a vast computer simulation piped directly into each human's brain. Neo, the unwitting key player in the fight against the Matrix (the simulators), meets Morpheus, leader of a band of free human rebels, who presents Neo with a choice: remain in the blissful false reality of the Matrix or exit the simulation and enter the real world.

Simulations play a key role in many areas of scientific research—including my own research in gamma-ray astronomy. We don't directly observe gamma rays. Instead, we see the results of their interaction as they pass through the atmosphere. In order to know how to make the most effective measurements, we simulate the gamma-ray/atmosphere interactions using computers. A good simulation incorporates all the relevant physics to produce predictions about what we will detect when we do make our measurements.

But what do simulations have to do with the multiverse? Remember, life must abound in the (strictly naturalistic) multiverse and some of that life must be far more advanced than humanity. Presumably, that advanced life will run many simulations and those simulations may be sufficiently complex as to model how life operates.

Alternate universes such as those in *The Matrix* may be fiction, but *if* the multiverse (as the strict naturalist envisions it) exists and *if* sufficiently complex simulations occur, then an astonishing scenario ensues: we may be unreal, bit-players in a simulation performed by some advanced life-form. Sir Martin Rees explains the consequences in this way:

> All these multiverse ideas lead to a remarkable synthesis between cosmology and physics. . . . But they also lead to the extraordinary consequence that we may not be the deepest reality, we may be a simulation. The possibility that we are creations of some supreme, or super-being, blurs the boundary between physics and idealist philosophy, between the natural and the supernatural, and between the relation of mind and multiverse and the possibility that we're in the matrix rather than the physics itself.[48]

Popping Into Existence

Another possibility, known as a Boltzmann Brain (BB), argues against the order scientists observe in the surrounding universe.[49] The concept of BBs rises from the possibility that atoms assemble by chance into a sentient being, due to thermal fluctuations permitted by the second law of thermodynamics. The popular rendition of the second law states that the total order of a system decreases over time. However, the order of some smaller part of a system may increase as long as the order of the whole system still decreases. Thus, with an absurdly small probability, atoms in a region of space will assemble into a being capable of observing the universe for some period of time (again assuming a purely physical basis for life). The probability dramatically decreases as the tenure of the observer's existence increases. Additionally, the probability of the observer seeing an orderly region decreases in regions displaying higher degrees of order.

In a finite universe the size of our observable universe, the probability of a BB is so small no one needs to consider it. However, one expects BBs to occur an infinite number of times in a spatially infinite multiverse where every conceivable state and history occurs. A BB in a solitary solar system surrounded by a disorderly universe would occur far more frequently than a BB in a solar system contained within an orderly spiral galaxy. Furthermore, most of the methods for comparing the number of ordinary observers (like human beings) to the number of BBs reveal that the BBs would far outnumber ordinary observers. Thus, the typical observer (including ordinary and BB observers) in such a naturalistic multiverse should not see the well-ordered universe that we observe.

If BBs exist, human life exhibits uniqueness. Either we are not typical observers (because we are not BBs) or we are BBs that see a unique, highly ordered universe. Models in which humans are unique or atypical indicate design. Ongoing research and refinements to these multiverse models can eliminate the possibility of the BBs. Their elimination would suggest human life is typical. However, these refined multiverse models require a high degree of fine-tuning in order to eliminate BBs.[50] Thus, it appears that multiverse models still exhibit design, whether or not human life is atypical.

DOES THE MULTIVERSE MEET THE CRITERIA?

Let's compare how naturalistic multiverse models stand up against the five requirements described earlier.

Self-Contained. If general relativity accurately describes this universe at all times, then the Hawking-Penrose theorems mandate a cosmic beginning. Similarly, any multiverse that, on average, experiences expansion must also have a beginning, according to the Borde-Vilenkin-Guth theorem. Inflation-generated multiverses all exhibit expansion on average so they all must have a beginning. Thus, they point to a transcendent Agent who causes them to exist.

Additionally, in order for the life contained on Earth to be typical in the multiverse, the mechanism that generates the multiverse must exhibit fine-tuning. Thus, multiverse models demonstrate design, which also points to a transcendent Designer.

Accounting for All Observations. Current observational data indicate a closed-geometry universe, contrary to the predictions of inflationary multiverse models. Additionally, the low power seen in the low spherical harmonics from WMAP indicate that the total universe may not be much larger than the observable universe. Thus, the observational evidence directly addressing the concept of an inflation-generated multiverse tends toward falsifying the models.

Multiverse Must Produce Sufficient Diversity. From their perspective, naturalist scientists can reasonably hypothesize that mechanisms exist to generate multiverses displaying a sufficient variety of physical laws, physical constants, and environments. However, such a mechanism is not currently known. So, this expectation must be buttressed with actual theoretical and observational evidence in the future.

Multiverse Must Produce the Observable Universe. Again, naturalist scientists may reasonably hypothesize that, given the existence of a multiverse, the observable universe—excluding life here on Earth—would be one of the possible natural outcomes. However, future testable evidence must substantiate these hypotheses.

Life Must Be Completely Physical. This requirement represents a difficult challenge for the naturalist. Scientists face a significant hurdle in demonstrating that life exists on a purely physical basis. Even more troublesome in a naturalistic multiverse context, purely physical life in a multiverse seriously undermines concepts central to the human experience, such as identity, justice, free will, and logic.

NATURAL OR DESIGNED?

A large proportion of the scientific community disagrees with or simply does not support multiverse theories. Some scientists argue that these models are unscientific because they offer no testable predictions. Others contend that simpler solutions explain the fine-tuning without invoking the existence of completely separate universes that, by definition, forever lie beyond scientists' ability to detect. Properly confronting these important issues in the scientific forum leads to better models and greater understanding of the physical universe. Some of the more substantive objections to various multiverse models reveal issues that multiverse advocates will certainly need to address.

In a Christian context, the apologist's battle does not directly concern the supposed or actual existence of the multiverse. Instead, it is the naturalist's claim that the multiverse provides an adequate, comprehensive, and consistent explanation for humanity's existence here on Earth without the need of a supernatural Designer. An important question is whether the multiverse inherently conflicts with the Bible. In principle, the answer is no.

Although Scripture does not directly address the concept of a multiverse, several passages provide hints that support the idea of multiple worlds. The Bible refers to an angelic realm (although it is spiritual) that exists beyond our universe. Also, Revelation 21–22 refers to a new physical world that God will create after this one is destroyed. These other realms imply that the existence of other universes represents no conflict with Scripture. Further, scientific research shows that God created a billion trillion stars in the observable universe, but the vast majority of them are not visible without powerful telescopes. Even more powerful telescopes are required to see the planets that exist around a fraction of those stars. Reasons To Believe's creation model argues that God created such a large universe with so many stars and planets in order for one Earth to exist and provide a suitable habitat for humanity. In a similar vein, why should we be troubled if God chose to create a multitude of universes so that this one would support life?

In practice, however, aspects of certain multiverse models raise troubling issues. The proposed existence of all possible histories and states assumes a completely physical basis for all life. In contrast, humanity's expressed reflection of the image of God is intrinsically nonphysical. Furthermore, the Bible clearly states that the human incarnation, death, and resurrection of God in Jesus occurred only once.[51] So positing histories and states with multiple human incarnations of Jesus also conflicts. However, this problem arises only in naturalistic multiverses, not those models that acknowledge God as Creator of the multiverse.

Whether the multiverse proves true or false substantially affects *none* of the fundamental Christian doctrines. For this reason it is important for believers to differentiate between multiverse models that advocate strict naturalism and models that promote the Creator. Rather than raising a battle cry against the concept of the multiverse, or writing it off as unfounded anti-biblical nonsense, it would behoove Christians to understand why people (scientists and others) find the multiverse such an attractive explanation for the observable universe.

While some multiverse theories initially appear to explain away the fine-tuned appearance of our observable universe and the events that make advanced life possible, they raise additional questions more complicated than the ones they answer. Do multiple versions of *me* making slightly different choices really exist? Do random processes spontaneously pop sentient beings into existence in the just-right place and moment to see a region of order? Are we just part of a highly complex, but nonetheless unreal, simulation?

SUPERNATURAL IS THE NEW NATURAL

Carl Sagan sums up the naturalist view, "the Cosmos is all that is or ever was or ever will be."[52] Traditionally, the cosmos referred to all the space, time, matter, and energy of this universe. However, inflation-generated multiverse theories now posit that another realm beyond this universe forced it into being. At this point, Christians agree with naturalists that something outside this realm "created" the universe; some naturalists cite the inflation-generated multiverse as that "something," while Christians point to the God of the Bible as the Creator.

The "realm beyond this universe" is, by definition, supernatural or beyond natural. The central question now concerns the nature of the supernatural "something." Is this entity personal or impersonal? Does it simply start the universe and "watch" from the outside or does it continually exist and intervene inside the universe? Questions similar to these provide excellent starting points for future scientific investigations—and spiritual conversations.

DOES THE MULTIVERSE DESTROY SCIENCE?

In order for a naturalistic multiverse model to adequately explain the fine-tuning for life observed in this universe, a vast number of other universes—each enormously large—must exist to sample all possible laws of physics, fundamental constants, and all conceivable histories and states. However, in such a model every possible situation will actually occur somewhere. If every possible situation occurs, no matter how improbable, on what basis does science operate?

The idea that a model can be either falsified or validated by future data provides a central theme in the scientific enterprise. Thus, by allowing for every possible situation, the multiverse ultimately explains nothing and undermines the whole scientific enterprise.

WHAT TO DO WITH THE MULTIVERSE

I distinctly remember a conversation over dinner at a conference I attended in 2001. Earlier in the day, a NASA astrobiologist had made a presentation dealing with the history of life on Earth. After his talk I asked what evidence he thought it would take to distinguish between a strictly naturalistic explanation for life's history and a creationist explanation. He responded that he had never really thought about it.

At dinner, the conversation turned to the implications of my question. The possibility of testing creation models intrigued some of my dining companions. Others said theological ideas had no place in the scientific endeavor. However, one comment still stands out in my mind. After issues of design and purpose arose, one prominent geologist off-handedly asked, "In which universe?"

I had begun reading about multiverse models in the scientific literature, but this was the first time I had personally encountered it as a response to the fine-tuning observed in our universe, and I had no answer. My hope is that this booklet will help you be better prepared.

At the time, the multiverse seemed a threat to my ability to defend my faith and maybe even to the doctrines of Christianity. Through my ongoing research, that sense of "threat" vanished. Scientific studies into the multiverse greatly strengthen the cosmological case for the universe having a beginning. Though some multiverse models appear to undermine the teleological argument, they still exhibit design and fine-tuning. Granted the design argument is more subtle and complex if a multiverse actually exists. However, as with the cosmological argument, studies of the multiverse ultimately make the teleological argument more robust. Consequently, as my understanding of the various multiverse models increased, I realized the whole issue provided a tremendous opportunity to engage science-minded people and draw them into discussion of the Gospel.

PRACTICAL ADVICE

Keep the Central Issue in Mind

Remember, the primary purpose of apologetics is to provide a reasonable defense of our faith and to help people take the Gospel seriously. Let's not carry the unnecessary burden of arguing against the existence of the multiverse—an idea on which the Bible is largely silent.

Ask Good Questions

Multiverse models attract various people for different reasons. Asking the right questions helps identify the issues important to the people you talk to. Try to determine which type of multiverse is being discussed. Seek to understand what questions the person thinks that model answers.

A more technically-oriented person might view certain multiverse models as the most scientifically legitimate explanation for the universe's fine-tuning. What do they consider the strongest evidence supporting those multiverse models? How do they respond to the theorems pointing to an ultimate beginning for *all* multiverse models?

For a lay person, focusing first on universally accepted philosophical ideas might prove more fruitful. Is it troubling that a strictly naturalistic multiverse significantly alters our basic intuitions about identity, justice, and free will? What if we are part of a *Matrix*-type simulation?

The goal of an apologist is not to win the argument over whether or not the multiverse exists. Rather, it's to demonstrate that the biblical description of the universe matches what scientists observe and, in this way, to buttress the authority of Scripture. We want to present the Gospel to those who are willing to consider seriously what the Bible has to say.

Keep Studying

From the cosmic battles between good and evil in *Star Wars* to the simulated realm of *The Matrix*, the happenings of other worlds intrigue countless people. The scientific interest in the multiverse parallels this widespread fascination with other worlds and greatly expands our idea of how vast and awesome this creation may be.

At first glance, the multiverse theory seems to effectively buttress the human "selection effect" explanation for the fine-tuned appearance of our universe. Yet as research into multiverse scenarios advances, it appears that they may simply move the design "up one level." In other words, instead of just one universe requiring fine-tuning to support life, it appears that any multiverse-generating mechanism also requires a high degree of fine-tuning to reproduce the observable universe in which we live.[53]

As with any other perceived challenge to Christianity, the multiverse should direct us to search out what both the Bible and science really say about creation. With God as the author of both, a proper interpretation of Scripture will never conflict with a proper understanding of his creation.

ENDNOTES

1. Carl Sagan, *Cosmos* (New York: Random House, 1980), 4.

2. Martin Rees, *Just Six Numbers* (New York: Basic Books, 2000).

3. Michael J. Denton, *Nature's Destiny* (New York: Free Press, 1998).

4. Peter D. Ward and Donald Brownlee, *Rare Earth* (New York: Copernicus, 2000).

5. Neil F. Comins, *What if the Moon Didn't Exist?* (New York: HarperCollins, 1993).

6. John D. Barrow and Frank J. Tipler, *The Anthropic Cosmological Principle* (New York: Oxford University Press, 1986).

7. John D. Barrow, *The Constants of Nature* (New York: Pantheon, 2002).

8. Hugh Ross, *The Creator and the Cosmos*, 3rd ed. (Colorado Springs: NavPress, 2001); and Hugh Ross, *Why the Universe Is the Way It Is* (Grand Rapids: Baker Books, 2008).

9. The most recent analysis of data from the cosmic microwave background radiation, galaxy clusters, and type Ia supernovae gives the following composition of the universe: 5% normal matter, 23% dark matter, 72% dark energy.

10. For more details regarding the development and testing of quantum mechanics, see John Gribbin, *In Search of Schrödinger's Cat* (Toronto: Bantam Books, 1984). Martin Gardner, *Relativity Simply Explained* (Mineola, NY: Dover, 1996) provides a similar discussion of the general theory of relativity.

11. For a readable introduction to string theory, see Brian Greene, *The Elegant Universe* (New York: Vintage Books, 1999).

12. The different multiverse levels described here follow the convention developed by MIT physicist Max Tegmark, "Parallel Universes," in *Science and Ultimate Reality*, ed. John D. Barrow, Paul C. W. Davies, and Charles L. Harper Jr. (Cambridge: Cambridge University Press, 2004).

13. I am not suggesting that Earth is the center of "the universe." The definition of an observable universe determines all the material that could possibly affect a specific location in space. A uniformly expanding cosmos with a constant speed of light gives a spherical observable universe around any specific location.

14. Measurements of the geometry of the universe indicate it is closed with a density within two percent of the critical density that would make it flat. Using the largest value of the curvature consistent with measurements (and assuming a simple topology like a ball), cosmologists can calculate a minimum size for the universe. The minimum calculated size would require at least one thousand regions the size of the observable universe to fill it. If future measurements show the observable universe closer to flat but still closed,

the minimum size of the universe will increase. Measurements of an open observable universe would imply a spatially infinite universe.

15. In order for two points to be in causal contact, the distance between them divided by the age of the universe must be less than one. Consider two points sixteen billion light-years apart in a fourteen billion year old universe giving a quotient of 1.143. Assuming the universe expands more slowly than the speed of light, when the universe was seven billion years old, the distance between the points must be larger than eight billion light years giving a quotient greater than 1.143. Thus, at earlier times in the universe, the two points were even farther out of causal contact than today.

16. For a more detailed account of scientists' view of inflation, the problems it solves, and the evidence supporting it, see Alan H. Guth, *The Inflationary Universe* (Reading, MA: Helix, 1997).

17. You might be wondering how the universe can expand at a rate faster than the speed of light when the speed of light serves as the cosmic speed limit. The short answer is that the speed of light only limits the motion of objects traveling *through* space. It imposes no limits on how quickly space can expand.

18. For a more complete discussion of this problem, see Guth, *The Inflationary Universe*, 189–200.

19. For a more complete discussion, see Guth, *The Inflationary Universe*, 201–35.

20. While that number is very small, it nonetheless provides a definite limit.

21. One interesting side note is that the combination of spatially infinite Level I multiverses and the Level II multiverse has a one-to-one correspondence with the Level III multiverse. In other words, if you compare the level of diversity in a Level III multiverse with the Level II multiverse, which contains multiple spatially infinite Level I multiverses, they both exhibit the same diversity.

22. Einstein expressed his dissatisfaction with the statistical nature of quantum theory. "Quantum mechanics is certainly imposing. But an inner voice tells me that it is not yet the real thing. The theory says a lot, but does not really bring us any closer to the secret of the 'old one.' I, at any rate, am convinced that *He* is not playing at dice." Albert Einstein's letter to Max Born, #52, December 4, 1926, in Max Born, *The Born–Einstein Letters, 1916–1955* (New York: Macmillan, 2005), 88.

23. Tegmark, "Parallel Universes."

24. Paul J. Steinhardt and Neil Turok, "A Cyclic Model of the Universe," *Science* 296 (May 24, 2002): 1436–39.

25. For Smolin's model, including its description, background, and testability, see Lee Smolin, *The Life of the Cosmos* (Oxford: Oxford University Press, 1997).

26. Stephen Hawking and Thomas Hertog, "Populating the Landscape: a Top-Down Approach," *Physical Review D* 73 (June 23, 2006): 123527–535.

27. Besides solving the horizon, flatness, and monopole problems, inflation also makes predictions about how the cosmic microwave background should appear—specifically regarding the number of acoustic peaks and the nearly scale invariant distribution of power in different spherical harmonics. D. N. Spergel et al., "Three-Year *Wilkinson Microwave Anisotropy Probe (WMAP)* Observations: Implications for Cosmology," *Astrophysical Journal Supplement Series* 170 (June 2007): 377–408 and E. Komatsu et al., "Five-year *Wilkinson Microwave Anisotropy Probe (WMAP)* Observations: Cosmological Interpretation," (to be published in *Astrophysical Journal Supplement Series*, preprint http://arxiv.org/abs/0803.0547) both demonstrate how the cosmic microwave background fulfills those predictions.

28. While this premise is largely noncontroversial and uncontested, it has a long history and some objectors. For more information see Ed L. Miller, *God and Reason*, 2nd ed. (Upper Saddle River, NJ: Prentice-Hall, 1972), 45–67.

29. Although Stephen Hawking contributed substantially to the development of the space-time theorems of general relativity—which demonstrate that the universe had a beginning—his more recent work seeks to find ways around the need for a beginning. He has explored using multiple time dimensions to remove the beginning (see *A Brief History of Time*, (Toronto: Bantam Books, 1988), 115–44) and using quantum effects to eliminate a unique beginning (see Stephen Hawking and Thomas Hertog, "Populating the Landscape: a Top-Down Approach," *Physical Review D* 73 (June 23, 2006): 123527–535).

30. Ross, *The Creator and the Cosmos*, 31–67.

31. Guth, *The Inflationary Universe*, 248–49. The universe Guth refers to here is the eternally existing multiverse.

32. Arvind Borde, Alan H. Guth, and Alexander Vilenkin, "Inflationary Spacetimes are Incomplete in Past Directions," *Physical Review Letters* 90 (April 18, 2003): 151301–4.

33. Ross, *The Creator and the Cosmos*. 145–67, 175–99.

34. See Fazale Rana with Hugh Ross, *Who Was Adam?* (Colorado Springs: NavPress, 2005), 97–111 and Hugh Ross, *Why the Universe Is the Way It Is* (Grand Rapids: Baker, 2008), 43–56.

35. It also appears to be exquisitely designed to permit humans to discover physical evidence for both the beginning of the universe and its design for human habitation. For more details, see Guillermo Gonzalez and Jay W. Richards, *The Privileged Planet* (Washington, D.C.: Regnery Books, 2004), 1–19, 195–218 and Hugh Ross, *Why the Universe Is the Way It Is* (Grand Rapids: Baker, 2008), 27–106.

36. Barrow and Tipler, *Anthropic Cosmological Principle*, 15–23.

37. Richard Swinburne, "Argument from the Fine-Tuning of the Universe," in *Physical Cosmology and Philosophy*, ed. John Leslie (New York: Macmillan, 1990), 165.

38. Swinburne, "Argument from the Fine-Tuning of the Universe," 165.

39. One should not mistake a spatially infinite universe for an infinitely old universe. Inflation produces a spatially infinite universe that is 13.7 billion years old. Viewed from outside our universe, the bubble that inflates and contains our universe will inflate forever. A general relativistic transformation converts the future time infinity outside the bubble into a spatial infinity inside the bubble. For more specific details on this process, see Martin A. Bucher and David N. Spergel, "Inflation in a Low-Density Universe," *Scientific American* 63 (January 1999): 62–69; and Jaume Garriga and Alex Vilenkin, "Many Worlds in One," *Physical Review D* 64 (July 26, 2001): 043511–15. For a more lay-level account, see Alex Vilenkin, *Many Worlds in One* (New York: Hill and Wang, 2006).

40. A royal flush consists of the ace, king, queen, jack, and ten of the same suit.

41. Daniel Kleppner, "A More Precise Fine Structure Constant," *Science* 313 (October 20, 2006): 448–49; N. Kanekar et al., "Constraints on Changes in Fundamental Constants from a Cosmologically Distant OH Absorber or Emitter," *Physical Review Letters* 95 (December 31, 2005): 261301; Phil Schewe and Ben Stein, "Have Particle Masses Changed Since the Early Universe?" *Physics News Update* 774 (April 19, 2006): #1; B. Altschul, "Limits on Lorentz Violation from Synchrotron and Inverse Compton Sources," *Physical Review Letters* 96 (May 26, 2006): 201101.

42. Leonard Susskind, *The Cosmic Landscape* (New York: Little, Brown, 2005), 371.

43. Komatsu et al., "Five-year *Wilkinson Microwave Anisotropy Probe (WMAP)* Observations."

44. This description only applies to universes containing just mass. If a space-energy density component exists, even closed universes can expand forever. The total density then becomes the sum of the mass density and the space-energy density; this sum determines the geometry of the universe.

45. Jean-Pierre Luminet et al., "Dodecahedral Space Topology as an Explanation for Weak Wide-angle Temperature Correlations in the Cosmic Microwave Background," *Nature* 425 (October 9, 2003): 593–95. S. Caillerie et al., "A New Analysis of the Poincaré Dodecahedral Space Model," *Astronomy & Astrophysics* 476 (2007): 691–96. B. Lew and B. Roukema, "A Test of the Poincaré Dodecahedral Space Topology Hypothesis with the WMAP CMB Data," *Astronomy & Astrophysics* 482 (2008): 747–53.

46. George Ellis, "Physics Ain't What It Used to Be," review of *The Cosmic Landscape*, by Leonard Susskind, *Nature* 438 (December 8, 2005): 739–40.

47. While the idea a of future time infinity transforming to present spatial infinity seems bizarre, it is well grounded in calculations using general relativity. For a more detailed discussion, see Bucher and Spergel, "Inflation in a Low-Density Universe" and Garriga and Vilenkin, "Many Worlds in One."

48. Martin Rees, "In the Matrix," *Edge*, May 19, 2003, 4–5, http://www.edge.org/documents/archive/edge116.html.

49. For a more recent discussion of issues surrounding Boltzmann Brains, see Don N. Page, "Return of the Boltzmann Brains," *Physical Review D* 78 (September 2008): 063536–39.

50. For example, see Robin Collins, "Design and the Many-Worlds Hypothesis," in *Philosophy of Religion: a Reader and Guide*, ed. William Lane Craig (New Brunswick, NJ: Rutgers University Press, 2002), 134–40.

51. For example, see 1 Peter 3:18; Hebrews 9:12, 27, 28.

52. Sagan, *Cosmos*, 4.

53. For example, see Collins, "Design and the Many-Worlds Hypothesis," 134–40.

GLOSSARY

Discrete – Describes a quantity that occurs in non-divisible increments. For example, matter appears to be continuous on macroscopic scales, but it comes in discrete bundles called atoms.

Expansion – Term characterizing the fact that the distance between any two locations in the universe grows over time because the amount of space between them increases.

Fundamental forces – The four known physical forces (gravitational, electro-magnetic, strong nuclear, and weak nuclear) that determine the behavior of all space, time, matter, and energy. The term "fundamental" is a misnomer because the four physical forces represent different manifestations of a more basic unified force (see the term "unification" below).

Inflation – A brief period of time in the early history of the cosmos wherein, the scale of the universe increased faster than the speed of light. Most cosmological models propose that the size of the universe increased by at least a factor of 10^{26} in less than 10^{-32} seconds.

Multiverse – The idea that the traditional universe (i.e., the observable universe) does not constitute all physical reality. The multiverse encompasses anything from a vast expanse that includes the observable universe plus regions beyond it to other universes that exist completely separate from our own.

Observable universe – A term specific to Earth-bound observers. It includes all locations in the universe where light has had time to traverse the distance from that position to Earth.

Observable volumes – A way to reference observable universes that are not associated with Earth.

Spatially infinite – A universe wherein the spatial dimensions extend forever in every direction without coming to an edge or looping back on themselves.

Spherical harmonic – A mathematical tool used to analyze how a quantity varies over the surface of a three-dimensional object. Just as determining the number and strength of the harmonics in a piece of music helps identify the instruments that produced the music, measuring the spherical harmonics associated with the cosmic microwave background radiation helps cosmologists understand the formation and development of the universe.

Total universe – Synonymous with the term "universe" (defined below).

Unification – A process through which scientists seek to build a theoretical framework (with experimental verification) in which the fundamental forces represent different manifestations of a more basic interaction. For example, scientists unified the electromagnetic and weak nuclear forces by demonstrating that they are different manifestations of the more fundamental electroweak force.

Universe – All regions of space governed by the same laws of physics and their associated fundamental constants. Includes the observable universe, but may also extend beyond it.

ABOUT THE AUTHOR

 **Dr. Jeff Zweerink** is a research scholar at Reasons To Believe (RTB). Since childhood, he wanted to understand how the worlds of science and Scripture integrate. A struggle began when Jeff's scientific studies seemed to collide with his early biblical training. Then he heard Hugh Ross speak. Learning about RTB and the harmony of the Christian faith and science resolved the difficulties.

Jeff pursued a B.S. in physics and a Ph.D. in astrophysics at Iowa State University, where he focused his study on gamma rays—messengers from distant black holes and neutron stars. Upon completing his education, Jeff taught at Loras College in Dubuque, Iowa. Postdoctoral research took him to the West Coast, to the University of California, Riverside, and eventually to a research faculty position at UCLA. He has conducted research using the STACEE and VERITAS gamma-ray telescopes, and participated in such research efforts as the Solar Two Project and the Whipple Collaboration.

On behalf of RTB, Jeff speaks at churches, universities, and professional groups around the country, encouraging people to consider how the Bible connects with the evidence of science.

Articles coauthored by Jeff have appeared in such journals as *Physical Review* and *The Astrophysical Journal*. He has also coauthored numerous conference proceedings, and still serves part-time on the physics and astronomy research faculty at UCLA. He also contributes to RTB's webcasts and podcasts as well as *Today's New Reason to Believe*.

Jeff and his wife, Lisa, live in Southern California with their five children.

ABOUT
REASONS TO BELIEVE

A science-faith think tank founded in 1986, Reasons To Believe (RTB) focuses on the relationship between the words of the Bible and the facts of nature. Whether in writing or in talks at universities, research labs, churches, and elsewhere, RTB scholars present reasons for confidence in the findings of science and in the authority of Scripture. These scientists and theologians demonstrate how God's verbal revelation proves accurate and wholly consistent with the latest discoveries. Podcasts, webcasts, video clips, and articles, including *Today's New Reason to Believe*, show how scientific advance supports the Christian faith. Each can be accessed at www.reasons.org. Event information is also listed. RTB's science-faith hotline ([626] 335-5282) operates daily from 5 to 7 P.M.

For an informative brochure and a description of available resources, call (800) 482-7836 or visit www.reasons.org.

DISCOVER MORE
REASONS TO BELIEVE

THE BIGGER PICTURE ON CREATION
By Krista Kay Bontrager

Designed for study groups of all kinds, this seven-lesson guide takes readers on an exploration of Genesis 1–2 and other key passages. Theologian and educator Krista Kay Bontrager challenges participants to think deeply about how Scripture connects with the record of nature.

MAJESTY OF THE MAKER
By Ken Hultgren

Many Christians shy away from the issue of creation because of strong disagreements not only between Christians and non-Christians, but also between people within the church. This study guide is designed to help anyone see the amazing beauty of God's creation and to share the good news of our Creator with others.

DUAL REVELATION (DVD)

This newly released docudrama highlights the historic Christian doctrine of divine revelation. With dramatic sequences to entertain and interviews with leading Christian scholars to enlighten, *Dual Revelation* shows how science can be a springboard for effective outreach as well as for spiritual growth.

For more information about **Reasons To Believe** or to order any of these resources, call **(800) 482-7836** or visit our Web store at **www.reasons.org**.